A World of Nonsense

Books by Carl Withers

A World of Nonsense
The Wild Ducks and the Goose
The Tale of a Black Cat
I Saw a Rocket Walk a Mile
A Rocket in My Pocket

A WORLD OF NONSENSE

Strange and Humorous Tales from Many Lands

CARL WITHERS

ILLUSTRATED BY JOHN E. JOHNSON

HOLT, RINEHART AND WINSTON
NEW YORK CHICAGO SAN FRANCISCO

Published simultaneously in Canada by Holt, Rinehart
and Winston of Canada, Limited.
Library of Congress Catalog Card Number: 68-11838
Printed in the United States of America
9679903
First Edition

Acknowledgments

Grateful acknowledgment is given to all folklore collectors, authors, and publishers whose work has been utilized in this book. Exact references to all sources are given in the Notes and Comments. If any required acknowledgments have been omitted or any rights overlooked, it is by accident and forgiveness is requested.

Special appreciation and gratitude are due to friends who have given much help: to Professor Herbert Halpert of Memorial University of Newfoundland, for the story "Old Wall Eyes" from the Ray Wood Manuscript in the Herbert Halpert Folklore Archives, and for illuminating private instruction over many years in the content, meaning, and function of folklore; to Professor Sula Benet of Hunter College, for much valuable listening and talking during the progress of making this book, and for translating the two Russian stories printed here; to Professor Alta Jablow of Brooklyn College for various suggestions that have been utilized, and for permission to quote a very informative passage about African dilemma stories from the Foreword of her book, *Yes and No Stories, the Intimate Folklore of Africa*; to Professor Nicholas S. Hopkins of New York University, for suggesting the delightful "Improbable African

Stories" from Mali; to Edwin Denby of New York City for help in translating from Italian "The Ship That Sailed on Water and on Land"; and to Professor Joseph Bram of New York University and Mr. Alfred Quittner of Kew Gardens, N.Y., for giving valuable help in translating a number of colloquial, archaic, and other difficult passages from German.

Additional warm thanks are due to the staff of the New York Public Library, ever patient, courteous, knowledgeable, and helpful in making the library's treasures available to the researcher.

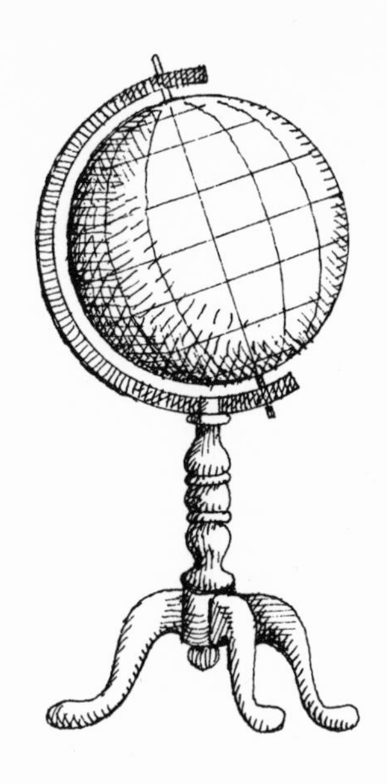

Contents

A World of Nonsense

There were three ponds on the point of a thorn: two of them were dry and the third held no water. Three potters settled in the one which held no water: two of them had no hands and the third was handless. The one who was handless made three pots: of these two were broken and the third had no bottom. In the last pot three grains of rice were put to cook: two stayed raw and the third one would not cook. Three guests were invited to eat the one which would not cook: two were angry and the third was ill-tempered. The ill-tempered one was given three blows with a shoe: two blows missed him and the other one didn't hit him. Soon the host's attention was taken up by a wild elephant that had attacked him. He struck the elephant with his fist and broke two and a half of his ribs. The wounded elephant fled and the man pursued him. The elephant ran up a tree and crawled from branch to branch and from twig to twig and from leaf to leaf—with his enemy following him. At last the elephant jumped down from the tree and, seeing a teapot with its top off, he ran in at the top and out through the spout. The elephant's body got through all right but his tail got stuck in the spout. His pursuer was too proud to kill a helpless animal and went his way.

India

The Mighty Wrestlers

Once upon a time, long, long ago, there was a mighty wrestler living in a far country, who, hearing that there was another mighty man in India, determined to have a match with him. So, tying up in his blanket ten thousand pounds of flour as food for the journey, he put the bundle on his head and set off jauntily. Towards evening he came to a little pond in the middle of the desert, and sat down to eat his dinner. First, he stooped down and took a good long drink of the water. Then, emptying his flour into what was left of the pond, he stirred it into a good thick porridge. Off this he made a hearty meal, lay down under a tree, and soon fell fast asleep.

Now, for many years an elephant had drunk daily at the pond, and, coming as usual that evening for its draught, was surprised to find nothing but a little flour and mud at the bottom.

"What shall I do?" the elephant said to itself. "There is no other water to be found within twenty miles."

Going away unhappily, the elephant spied the wrestler

sleeping placidly under the tree, and at once decided that he was the author of the mischief. So, galloping up to the sleeping man, it stamped on his head in a furious rage, determined to crush him.

But, to the elephant's astonishment, the wrestler only stirred a little and said sleepily, "What's the matter? What's the matter? If you want to massage my head, why in thunder don't you do it properly? What's worth doing at all is worth doing well, my friend. So put a little of your might into it!"

The elephant stared, and left off stamping. But, still angry, it seized the wrestler round the waist with its trunk, intending to heave him up and dash him to pieces on the ground.

"Ho! ho! my little friend! So that is your plan, is it?" said the wrestler, with a yawn. And he caught hold of the elephant's tail, swung the monster over his shoulder, and continued his journey jauntily.

By and by he reached the Indian wrestler's house, and standing outside it he cried out, "Ho! my friend! Come out and have a wrestling match with me!"

"My husband's not home today," answered the wrestler's wife from inside. "He has gone into the wood to cut stakes for his pea vines."

"Well, well! When he returns give him this, with my compliments. And tell him the giver has come from afar to challenge him."

So saying, he chucked the elephant clean over the courtyard wall.

"Oh, Mamma, Mamma!" cried a treble voice from within, "that nasty man outside has thrown a mouse over the wall into my lap! What shall I do to him?"

"Never mind, little daughter!" answered the wrestler's wife. "Papa will soon teach him better manners. Take the grass broom and sweep the mouse away."

There was a sound of sweeping, and immediately the dead elephant came flying over the wall.

"Oh, my!" thought the wrestler outside, "if the little daughter can do this, the father will be a worthy foe!"

So he set off toward the wood to meet the Indian wrestler, whom he soon saw coming along the road, dragging a hundred and sixty carts laden with brushwood.

"Now we shall see!" said the stranger, with a wink, and, stealing to the end of the line of carts without being seen, he took hold of the last cart and began to pull.

"That's a deep rut!" thought the Indian wrestler, and pulled a little harder. So it went on for an hour, each pulling against the other, but not an inch one way or the other did the carts budge.

"I believe there's someone hanging on behind!" said the Indian wrestler at last, and he walked back to see who it was. Whereupon the stranger, coming to meet him, said, "We seem pretty well matched. Let us have a bout together."

"With all my heart!" answered the other, "but not here alone in the wilds. There is no fun in fighting without an audience to applaud."

"But I haven't time to wait," said the stranger. "I have to be off at once, so it must be here or nowhere."

Just then an old woman came hurrying by with big strides.

"Here's an audience!" cried the wrestler, and called aloud, "Mother! mother! stop and see fair play!"

"I can't, my sons, I can't!" she replied, "because my

daughter is about to steal my camels, and I am off to stop her. But if you like, you can just jump onto the palm of my hand, and wrestle there as I go along."

So the wrestlers jumped up onto the palm of the old woman's hand, and wrestled away as she strode over hill and dale.

Now when the old woman's daughter saw her mother coming, with the wrestlers wrestling on her hand, she said to herself, "Here she comes, with the soldiers she threatened to bring! It's time for me to be off!"

So she picked up the hundred and sixty camels she was herding, tied them up in her blanket, swung it over her shoulder, and set off at a run.

But one of the camels put his head out of the blanket and began groaning and groaning and *hubble-bubble-ubbling*, after the manner of camels. So, to quiet it, the girl tore down a tree or two, and stuffed them into the bundle also. On seeing this, the farmer to whom the tree belonged came running up and calling, "Stop thief! Stop thief!"

"Thief, indeed!" said the girl angrily, and with that she snatched up the farmer, together with his fields, crops, oxen, and house, and bundled them all into the blanket.

Soon she came to a town. By now she was hungry, and she asked a pastry cook to give her some sweets. When he refused, she caught him up bodily and the town itself and stuffed them into the blanket. And she did the same thing with everything she met, until her blanket was quite full.

At last she came to a big watermelon, and being both thirsty and hungry, she sat down to eat it. Afterwards, feeling sleepy, she decided to rest a while, but the camels in her bundle made such a hubble-bubble-ubbling that they disturbed her. So she just packed everything into the lower half of the watermelon rind, and popped the upper half on as a lid. Then she rolled herself up in the blanket and, using the melon as a pillow, she went to sleep.

While she slept, a big flood arose, and carried off the watermelon, which floated downstream ever so far, until at last it stuck on a mudbank, and the top fell off. Now out hopped the camels, the trees, the farmer, the oxen, the house, the town, and all the other things, until there was quite a new world on that mudbank in the middle of the river.

India

What News? News Enough!

A master-tinker asked his two workmen who had just come back from a trip:

"What news, comrades?"

First workman: "No news! News enough! My news, master, is that I saw a mill grinding in a treetop."

Master: "That's a big fib! We'll have no fibbers here!"

First workman: "Ask my comrade if what I've just said isn't true."

Master: "Is it true, comrade, what your comrade said?"

Second workman: "I don't know what he said, master."

Master: "He said he saw a mill grinding in a treetop."

Second workman: "I didn't see that, master, but I did see a rat climbing down from a tree with his whiskers covered with flour."

Master: "Was he coming down from that mill?"

Second workman: "I suppose so."

Master: "What other news, comrades?"

First workman: "No news! News enough! My news, master, is that I saw a horse seven leagues in circumference."

Master: "That's a big fib! We'll have no fibbers here!"

First workman: "Ask my comrade if what I've just said isn't true."

Master: "Is it true, comrade, what your comrade said?"

Second workman: "I don't know what he said, master."

Master: "He said he saw a horse seven leagues around."

Second workman: "I didn't see that, master, but I saw a hundred saddle makers busy making a single saddle."

Master: "Were they making it to put on the back of that horse?"

Second workman: "I suppose so."

Master: "What other news, comrades?"

First workman: "No news! News enough! My news, master, is that I saw a great pot of soup boiling on a rock in the sea."

Master: "That's a big fib! We'll have no fibbers here!"

First workman: "Ask my comrade if what I've just said isn't true."

Master: "Is it true, comrade, what your comrade said?"

Second workman: "I don't know what he said, master."

Master: "He said he saw a great pot of soup boiling on a rock in the sea."

Second workman: "I didn't see that, master, but I saw a hundred rats carrying copper spoons."

Master: "Was it to eat that soup?"

Second workman: "I suppose so."

France

The Ship that Sailed on Water and on Land

One time a king issued this proclamation: "Whoever is clever enough to build a ship that will travel on water and on land shall have my daughter for his wife."

In that realm there was a father with three sons, and all that he had in the world was a horse, a donkey, and a little pig.

When the eldest son heard about the proclamation, he said to his father, "Papa, sell the horse, and with the money you get for the horse buy me the tools to make a ship. With those tools I'll make a ship that sails on water and on land, and I will marry the king's daughter."

He begged so hard, day after day, that at last, to keep peace in the family, the father sold the horse and bought him the tools. The son got up early, took the tools and went into the woods to cut the wood to make the ship.

He had the ship about half built, when a little old man came by.

"What fine thing are you making, my boy?" asked the old man.

"Barrel staves!" said the boy impolitely.

"Then barrel staves you'll find already made," said the old man, and went away.

The next morning the son returned to the woods where he had left the half-finished boat, the rest of the wood, and his tools. He found nothing but a pile of barrel staves. He went home weeping in despair and told his father what had happened. Imagine the father's anger, who had lost a horse because of the son's caprice. A little more and he would have skinned him alive!

In less than a month, the middle son got that same idea of trying to build a ship that would sail on water and on land. So he went to the father and begged and sighed until at last the father felt he must sell the donkey and buy him the necessary tools. And now *he* took the tools and went into the forest to cut the wood. He had the boat half-built when the same little old man passed by.

"What are you making, my fine boy?" he asked.

"Broomsticks!" said the boy.

"Broomsticks you'll find already made," said the old man, and went on his way.

The boy went home that evening, ate and slept, and returned the next morning to the woods. The same thing happened to him as to his elder brother. All that he found was a pile of broomsticks. He returned home half out of his mind and told his father.

"That's fine!" cried the father. "You both got just what you deserved, in following your crazy notions. And I got what I deserved for listening to you."

The youngest brother heard all this, and said,

"Well, we've lost so much we'd just as well lose a little bit more. So, Papa, please let me have a try. Let's sell the

little pig and get me some tools. Maybe I can do what the other two have failed to do."

Well, the little pig was sold, and the youngest brother took the tools and went into the woods. He had the ship half-done, when the little old man appeared again.

"My fine boy, what are you making?" the old man asked.

"I am making a ship that sails on water and on land," replied the boy.

"You'll find a ship that sails on water and on land already made," said the old man, and went away.

The boy went home at evening to eat and sleep, and came back at early dawn. He found the ship completely finished, with the sails spread.

He went on board and said, "Ship, sail on land." The ship, just as if it were sailing on the water, floated lightly through the woods. He sailed it home and showed it to his father and brothers, who stood there goggle-eyed.

Now the youngest brother again said to the ship, "Sail on land!" and he started off in it toward the king's palace. Whenever he came to a river, the ship swam across. Wherever there was plains or mountains, the ship floated over them.

He now had a ship, but he lacked a crew. He came to a large river, at a point where a smaller river flowed into it. But the smaller river didn't reach the large river because a little way upstream a big man was kneeling down on the bank and drinking up all the water.

"What a big throat you have, my good man!" said the boy. "Do you want to come with me? I'll take you to the king's palace."

The man took another great draft, went *gulp*, and said, "Gladly, now that I've quenched my thirst a little." And he came aboard the ship.

The ship sailed over water and over land and came to a big man who was turning a spit over a fire. On the spit was a large buffalo.

"Hey!" called the boy from the deck, "do you want to go with me to the king's palace?"

"Gladly," said the man. "Just wait till I eat this little bird."

"Certainly," said the boy.

The man gobbled the buffalo off the spit in one mouthful as if it were a thrush. Then he went on board and the ship sailed on over lakes and fields.

It came to another big man who was sitting down with his shoulders pressed against a mountain.

"Hey!" said the owner of the boat, "will you go with me to the king's palace?"

"I can't move from here!" replied the man.

"Why not?" the boy asked.

"Because I'm holding up the mountain with my shoulders. If I move, it will fall."

"Then let it fall!" said the boy.

The man held his hand against the mountain, got up

and jumped on board. The ship had scarcely started sailing again when they heard a great roar—BOOM! The mountain had already fallen.

The ship sailed on over roadways and hills and arrived before the palace of the king. The boy got off and said, "Your Sacred Highness, I have been clever enough to make this ship that sails on water and on land. So now, you'll keep your promise and give me your daughter as my wife."

The king hadn't expected anything like this! He was crestfallen. He didn't know what to do. He was sorry he had ever issued that proclamation. He certainly didn't want to give his daughter to a nobody that he had never even heard of.

"Well, I'll give you my daughter," the king said, "on condition that you and your company can eat a banquet I'll give for you. But you must not leave even a chicken wing or a grape seed uneaten!"

"That's fine!" said the boy. "When will that banquet be?"

"Tomorrow," said the king.

The king ordered his servants to prepare a dinner with a million courses. "This scarecrow," he thought, "surely won't have a company able to eat all that stuff."

The owner of the ship appeared at the dinner with only one companion—the man who had eaten the buffalo as if it were a thrush. The fellow ate and ate. He ate up ten courses one after the other, then he gulped down a hundred more, and then he dusted off another thousand.

The king, who had stood there watching him without a word, pulled himself together and said to the waiters, "Isn't there anything else in the kitchen?"

"There are some leftovers."

The leftovers were brought to the table, and the fellow still had enough room in his stomach to eat up even the crumbs.

The king said, "It's clear that you are going to marry my daughter if you want to, but first I'd like to offer you and your company the wine from my cellar, on condition that you drink it all, without leaving even the dregs in a glass."

The man came who had drunk up the river, and he began by draining a barrel, and then a keg, and then a demijohn. He finished by swallowing two bottles of fine malmsey that the king had laid aside for himself, and he asked for more.

"You ought to see by now that I have no objections to giving you my daughter," said the king. "But there's also a dowry that goes with her—all such things as her chests,

her bed, her washbowl, her linen, her treasure chests, and everything she has in the house. You'll have to carry away everything she owns in one load, without leaving a single thing behind, and my daughter must go along on top of it all."

"Does that seem much of a task to you?" the boy asked the man who had held up the mountain.

"Heavens, no!" he replied. "That's just the kind of job I'm crazy about doing."

So they came up to the palace and the boy said to the servants, "Are you ready? Yes? Then let's start loading the stuff on this fellow's shoulders."

They began to pile onto him wardrobes, tables, jewel cases. They loaded onto his back a mountain of things that reached up to the roof of the palace. And to get on top of it all the princess had to climb up and come out of the palace tower.

When she was up there, the man said, "Hold on tight, Princess!" and started off. He carried all that heap of things to the ship and jumped aboard.

"Now, sail, my ship!" said the boy, and the ship began to glide away over the palace garden, and over the roads and countryside.

The king, watching from his window, cried out to his soldiers, "Quick! my faithful ones! Follow them! Catch them! Bring them back to me in chains!"

The army started out in pursuit, but all they were able to catch was a little dust blown up as the ship floated over the ground. So the soldiers stopped and gazed in astonishment with their tongues hanging out.

When the father saw his youngest son return with the ship full of treasure and with the king's daughter in her bridal dress, his heart filled with happiness. The boy had a palace built which was the last word in splendor. He gave a floor in it to his father and brothers and a floor to each of his traveling companions. He kept the rest for himself and his wife.

Italy

The Donkey's Egg

There was once a young man who saw some pumpkins growing in a farmer's field. He had never seen pumpkins before and he asked the farmer, "What are those things?"

"Donkey's eggs," answered the farmer.

"Donkey's eggs? If you hatch them out, do little donkeys come out of them?"

"Yes," said the farmer.

"Then sell me one."

The young man took the pumpkin home and told his wife to sit on it. She sat on the pumpkin for a fortnight. Then he took her place and sat on it for a week. At the end of that time he was tired of sitting there and he still saw no signs that the egg was about to hatch.

"The egg doesn't seem to be a good one," he said. So he took it out into the orchard and tossed it down a deep bank.

The pumpkin broke rolling downhill and scared a little rabbit from under a bush, who ran off as fast as it could.

"What a shame!" cried the man. "If I had sat on it just three days more I would have had a nice little donkey. It has fine long ears, but it has only a little wisp of tail."

France

A Trip to the Sky

Once a peasant let a rooster go under the floor of his cottage, and there the rooster found a little pea seed and began calling to all his hens to come. The peasant heard the commotion, drove the rooster away, and poured some water on the pea.

So the little pea started to grow. It grew and grew, and grew up to the floor. The man had to make a hole in the floor, so that the pea could keep growing. Now it grew and grew and grew until it reached the ceiling, and the man had to make a hole in the ceiling so that it could keep growing. Again it grew and grew until it reached the roof, and the man made a hole in the roof of his house so that the little pea could grow some more. It kept right on growing and growing until it reached the sky.

The man saw where it had gone and turned around and said to his wife, "Wife! Wife! I think I'll climb up to the sky and see what's going on up there. Maybe there's sugar up there, and mead, and plenty of everything!"

"Climb away, if you feel like it," replied his wife.

So the man started climbing. He climbed and he climbed, and after a long hard climb he finally reached the sky. There he saw a large house and walked in and looked around in great wonder. He saw so much that his eyes were almost blinded with looking. In the house there was a great stove, and on this stove there was a goose and suckling pigs and pies. He saw, in short, everything the heart could desire.

The stove was guarded by a goat with seven eyes, but the man quickly decided what he must do. He chanted a spell: "Sleep, little eye! Sleep, little eye!" And one eye of the goat went to sleep. He chanted a little louder, "Sleep, little eye! Sleep, little eye!" and another one of the goat's eyes went to sleep. In the same way he put six of the goat's eyes to sleep, but he didn't see the seventh eye, which was on the goat's back, and so he failed to charm it asleep.

Now he went to the stove and ate and drank everything he could hold, and then he stretched out on a bench and went to sleep.

When the owner of the house came home, the goat told him everything he had seen with his seventh eye, and the owner was very angry. He called his servants and they threw the peasant out. He ran to the place where he had left the pea vine. He looked and looked for it, but the pea vine was gone! What could he do? How was he going to get down?

He looked around and began to collect the cobwebs which were floating in the summer air. He twisted the cobwebs into a rope and fastened this rope to the edge of the sky and started to climb down. Hand over hand he climbed down the rope, down and down, but long before he reached the earth he came to the end of the rope. He looked down, and the ground was very far away. There was nothing to do but jump, so crossing himself he let go the rope and fell and fell, and he landed in a bog.

Whether he was a long time or a short time in the bog is not easy to say, but there he sat in the mud up to his neck. At last a duck decided to build her nest on his head. So she built a nest and laid some eggs in it. One day the peasant got a good idea, and when the duck came to her nest he grabbed her by the tail. She beat her wings this way and that way to get free, and in trying to get free she pulled the peasant out of the mud. He took the duck and her eggs home, and told his wife all that had happened.

It's no wonder of wonders that he fell down from the sky;
The wonder of wonders is, how did he get up there so high?

Russia

Air Castles

A poor peasant walking in an open field saw a hare under a bush and was filled with joy. He said: "I'm really in luck! I'll catch this hare and kill him and sell him for four coins. With that money I'll buy a little pig and she will grow up and bring me twelve little pigs. And when those twelve little pigs grow up each of them will bring me twelve little pigs. When they are grown I'll butcher them and then I'll have a whole barnful of meat. I'll sell the meat, and with the money from the meat I'll set myself up in a house, and then I'll get married. My wife will bring me two sons, Vaska and Vanka. The boys will work the land and I'll sit at the window and give them orders. I'll cry, 'You boys—Vaska and Vanka! Don't overwork your men! It seems you boys have never known what it is to be poor!' " And the peasant shouted his words so loud that he frightened the hare, who ran away. And so his house with all his riches and his wife and children disappeared.

Russia

Old Wall Eyes

One time a country fellow started into town with a wagon-load of beef to peddle. He was driving a fast team of mules. He had to pass through a big woods where Old Wall Eyes had his den. Old Wall Eyes had a mouth as big as a butter-milk churn and it got bigger and bigger the more he ate. And eyes—why, his eyes were as big as teacups and they went round and round, faster and faster. If he ran fast they went faster and faster, and if he walked slow they went round slow. They got bigger, too! The closer he got to you the bigger his eyes got, and everybody was afraid of him. But he couldn't climb a tree. No sir-ree, he couldn't climb a tree! He just had to run on the ground like a horse, but there never was any horse that could run like Old Wall Eyes.

Well now, when the fellow had just got out of sight in the woods he heard Old Wall Eyes begin to squall. He knew right then that the creak of the wagon wheels had woke up Old Wall Eyes.

And soon here came Old Wall Eyes, with his eyes a-whirling round and round like wheels! Here he came, just a-tearing up the bushes and a-pitching them behind him.

The fellow took one look and started up his mule team with a crack and a lash. Old Wall Eyes was after his wagon-load of beef and the man had to reach a clearing in the timber in a hurry. Old Wall Eyes didn't prowl anywhere out-side the deep timber so he would be plumb safe if he could just beat Old Wall Eyes to that clearing. The little old mules

ran lickety-split and the wagon went a-bumping over rocks and deep ruts and stumps. They were just a-splitting that timber road wide open, and Old Wall Eyes was right behind them and getting closer all the time.

His eyes were as big as saucers and his mouth was as big as a washpan. He was a-squalling worse than a hungry panther, and he was a-tearing up the bushes and a-pitching them behind him. Soon he caught up with the wagon, and you could tell that he was aiming to jump right square dab into the middle of that wagonload of beef.

So the fellow picked up a beef shoulder and pitched it out to Old Wall Eyes. Old Wall Eyes just stopped long enough to swallow up that beef and then here he came again. His eyes were as big as bread plates, and his mouth was as big as a bushel basket. He was just a-tearing up the bushes and a-pitching them behind him.

So the fellow pitched out a hindquarter of beef. Old Wall Eyes caught it and swallowed it down and here he came on the run! His eyes were a-turning like two big crocks, and his mouth was as big as a washkettle. He was just a-tearing up the bushes and a-pitching them behind him.

So now the fellow chunked out the whole half of the beef that was left. Even that didn't stop Old Wall Eyes for long, and on he came again. His eyes were a-rolling like two cotton baskets, and his mouth was as big and red as a fireplace. He was just a-stomping down the pine bushes and a-coming on.

Finally, the fellow reached down over the dashboard and unhooked one of the mules from the wagon. He jumped a-straddle of him and away they went, while Old Wall Eyes swallowed up the other mule just like a chicken snake would swallow a hen egg. And here he came again. Now his eyes were as big as two cookstoves and his mouth was as big as a wagon-gate. He had it wide-open, too, and he was a-gooshing like a big old mean river hog. He went, "Gooshie-gooshie-gooshie-gooshie!"

The fellow could feel Old Wall Eyes a-blowing his breath right down his shirt collar. Now he was sure enough a-tearing up the bushes and a-pitching them behind him. He was just going to swallow the man and the mule and the gear and all when—what do you think? That fellow saw a big old tall pine tree, and he didn't lose any time at all a-climbing up that tree. Old Wall Eyes just went round and round and round and round that tree a-tearing up the bushes and a-pitching them behind him. But the fellow was safe, because Old Wall Eyes couldn't climb a tree.

United States

Rival Storytellers

1. SEEING FAR AND HEARING FAR

Two men were standing on a river bank. The other bank of the river, a mile away, was a rock cliff.

One man said, "Can you see that mosquito a-walkin' around over there on that cliff?"

The other man said, "No, I can't see him, but I can sure hear him a-trompin'."

2. THE BIG PUMPKIN AND THE BIG KETTLE

A man started bragging about a crop of big pumpkins he had raised. One was so big he couldn't load it on his wagon, he said, so he left it in the field. That winter a sow disappeared, and the next spring he found her and ten little pigs living inside that pumpkin.

A listener said he had visited a factory where he saw men making a kettle a hundred feet in diameter.

"What would anybody want with a kettle that big?" asked the first man?

"They were making that kettle just to cook that big pumpkin of yours," replied the other.

3. FISH STORY

One fisherman told his friend, "I went fishing last night and caught a fish three feet long."

The friend said, "I went fishing last night, too, and with my hook I pulled out of the water a lantern that was still burning."

The first fisherman asked, "How could that lantern keep burning when it had been in the water?"

The second fisherman replied, "Well, you cut two feet off your fish, and I'll blow out my lantern."

4. THE BOASTFUL ALASKANS

One Alaskan said: "It gets so cold where I live that our words freeze coming out of our mouths. We have to throw them into the frying pan and thaw them out to know what we are talking about."

United States

5. THE BIG CHINESE DRUM

A man who was known to enlarge his stories said, "In my village there is a temple with a drum that is many miles in circumference."

A bystander replied, "In my village there is an ox so big that its tail is in one province and its head is in another. Its feet weigh over a ton. Now I call that *big*."

No one believed him and a bystander said, "No ox could be that big."

"If there is no ox that big," he retorted, "how do they get a skin to cover that big drum?"

6. TRAVELING TO SEE WONDERS

A man from Northern China heard so much about the huge bridges in Southern China that he set out to see them. On the way he met a man from the South who was traveling north to see the huge carrots that, he had heard, grew there.

The Southerner suggested that, instead of continuing their long journeys, each should describe the wonders of his region to the other.

"As for our bridges," he said, "a man fell off one a year ago, and his body has not yet reached the water. How's that for high?"

"It is indeed high," said the Northerner. "As for our large carrots, you are wasting your time in traveling to see them. By next year they will have grown big enough to be with you in the South.

China

7. A SHILLING FOR A LIE

One day a man saw two boys playing marbles and said, "I will give a shilling to the one of you who can tell me the biggest lie." The first one spoke: "My father is a hunter. He shot a flea three hundred and sixty-five miles away in the right eye and didn't kill it." The second boy said, "My father is a mason. He built a wall so high that God had to come down and ask him to take out two bricks so that the moon could pass over." The man divided the shilling between the two boys.

Grenada, British West Indies

The Greatest Boast

There was a woman who had three sons, and the only property she had to leave them was a pear tree. When she died she left a will which none of them could understand. Since each son wanted the pear tree, they took the will to a judge and asked him to interpret it.

The judge read the will and said, "The pear tree is to go to the one of you who can boast of the greatest achievement."

The eldest son made his boast first: "When I am chasing a hare, I can skin the hare without even checking his flight."

The second son boasted next: "If a man is galloping by on a horse, I can take the shoes off the horse without reducing the horse's speed."

The youngest one now spoke: "I can climb the highest mountain to a spot where all the winds are blowing, and if a featherbed is opened there and all the feathers are shaken out, I am so quick that, no matter how strong the winds nor how light the feathers, I can gather all the feathers back into the featherbed."

It was to him that the judge gave the pear tree.

Germany

The Pugilist and His Wonderful Helpers

Once upon a time a pugilist lived in Bremen who understood his art better than anyone else in the whole world. He had at last become so proficient in the ring that he could take on twenty-four opponents at once and win over them every time.

"Holla," he thought to himself, "I'll just take a trip and show my skill. Let others show off what they can do, for money. No one can perform wonders half so great as I can. Wherever I go, people will all hurry up to see my strength."

No sooner said than done. On a summer morning he flung his seven possessions onto his shoulders and walked out through the city gate.

Not far from the city he came to a huntsman who had his gun raised high in the air and was pointing it very carefully, although not a bird could be seen or heard. Our pugilist looked at him a moment and then with great curiosity asked what he was about to shoot.

"Don't disturb me, friend," said the huntsman, without even looking down from the sky. Suddenly he fired his gun and said, "There it is!"

"There's what?" asked the other. "I can't see anything."

"That's quite possible," answered the huntsman, "since it *is* rather far away. I just shot a sparrow on the steeple of the cathedral in Strassburg."

"Shall we travel together?" asked the pugilist. "You're

just the man for me. I, too, can do more than other people."

They quickly agreed to join forces, and set forth together very companionably. They had not gone a thousand paces when a fellow overtook them and swept on past as fast as a cannonball. They were amazed and watched him as far as their eyes could see him. But it wasn't over half a minute until even the huntsman, sharp as his eyes were, could no longer see him. They went along, still wondering at the man's great speed, but before they realized it he was back.

"Where have you been?" the two travelers asked.

"Not far," he answered. "Just to Rome. I had to deliver a letter there."

Their eyes opened wide when they heard that. It had been only ten minutes at the longest since he flew past.

"Will you travel with us?" they both asked him at the same time, and they told him about their own skills.

The runner thought a moment and agreed to go along with them. So now there were three traveling companions.

They hadn't gone over a mile further when they came to a big forest. At the edge of it stood a man with a rope in his hands that was tied around the whole forest. Just before they came up to him he gave the rope a big yank, and all the trees pulled out of the ground like turnips and fell over on one another. Only a very few trees remained standing, and the strong man reached out and grabbed them and pulled them out by the roots.

"Here's another man after our heart," said the travelers, and they asked him to go along with them. He accepted their invitation, and so all four went on together.

A little further on they came to a high mountain. On it stood a man with arms akimbo and his cheeks puffed out. He was blowing with all his strength. The travelers could feel the wind while they were still a good distance away from him, even though he was blowing in another direction. Curiosity drove the travelers up the mountain. They asked him where he was blowing and why he was blowing so terribly hard.

"I've got to!" he answered. "Don't you see the thirty-six windmills all roundabout? I have to keep them turning. When the wind helps me out by blowing even a little bit, my job isn't so hard. But today, unfortunately, no air is stirring and so I have a great labor." While he was talking to our travelers, all the windmills stopped. As soon as he blew again, they all started turning as before.

"We've got to take him along with us," the travelers whispered to each other. They asked him to join them, he accepted, and so they all started off—now five in number—toward Mainz.

Here they found everything in a sad uproar, because the duke lay ill. The doctors had completely given him up. The only means to save him, they said, was lacking. If they could get a certain herb, before noon, it might be possible to save the duke's life. But there was no hope of getting that herb in time because it grew only in the Swiss Alps. There was no way to fetch it so soon.

As soon as our travelers heard this they went to the castle and promised to get the needed herb within the time named if they were offered a suitable reward. Their message was taken in to the duke and he said that for this service he would give as much gold and silver as the strongest man could carry. The five friends were delighted with his offer and in a wink the fast runner was off to fetch the herb.

When an hour had passed the others began to be very impatient for their friend's return. It was already ten o'clock and he wasn't back. They waited another half hour, and when he didn't come they began to be scared. They sent the huntsman up onto the castle tower to look around for him with his sharp eyes. At first he couldn't see him anywhere. Then he saw him far off beyond Basel.

"The lazy rascal is lying there asleep!" he cried. "Just wait, we'll wake you up."

With that he loaded his gun and shot the hat off the fast runner's head. He was on his legs in a flash, and before the huntsman could climb down from the steeple he was there with the herb. This was carried in to the duke, who took it and was hale and hearty in an instant. Now he told the travelers that they could send someone in to take away the money. They knew no one better to do this than the strong man who had torn down the whole forest. So he went to the castle, went down into the treasury, and packed up everything that was there, so that not even a single coin remained. He wasn't content with this, however, but went round all over the castle and gathered up all the gold and silver he could find anywhere and carried it all away. Who could be happier than the other four men, when they saw the incredible amount of gold and silver? To lighten the strong man's load a little, they loaded themselves with part of the treasure. Then they all started walking toward the city gate in order to seek their fortune somewhere else.

Meanwhile, the duke learned how completely his castle had been plundered. He summoned two regiments of soldiers and sent them after the travelers to take back part of the money and valuables they were carrying away. They were only about a mile outside the gate when they saw the soldiers on their tracks. They saw at once that what they most needed was good advice.

"If it were only twenty-four men," said the pugilist, "I could make short shrift of them. But two regiments! That's too much for me."

"If I only had my rope," said the strong man who had pulled down the forest, "I would tie them all together so they couldn't even move, but—"

"What can I do?" asked the huntsman. "I can easily shoot down one man with every shot. But I don't have enough shells to shoot very many of them."

"I have nothing to fear," said the fast runner. "They won't get me because I can rely on my legs to carry me out of danger."

"What kind of a problem is this?" asked the man with strong lungs. "There's really nothing much to it."

So he set his arms akimbo and blew with might and main. Within a very few minutes he had blown the two regiments far, far away. And to this day nobody knows where they went.

Germany

Hans Hansen's Hired Girl

Hansen's Trina was lazy and wouldn't do anything. She said to herself, "Shall I eat or shall I sleep or shall I work? Oh, I shall eat first."

When she had eaten she said again, "Shall I work or shall I sleep? Oh, I shall sleep a little first." Then she lay down and slept, and when she woke, it was night and she could no longer go out to the field to work. And so went all the days.

One afternoon Hans came to the house and found Trina lying in her bed sleeping, so he took out his knife and cut her dress off up to her knees.

Trina woke up and thought, "Now I must go out and work."

When she had gone out and saw that her dress was now so short, she was frightened and wondered if she was really Trina.

She said to herself, "Am I I, or am I not I?" But she did not know how to answer herself.

She stood there in doubt a moment and then she thought, "I must go to the house and ask whether or not I am I. They will know."

So she went to the house, knocked at the window, and called in, "Is Hansen's Trina in there?"

They answered, "Yes, she is lying in her room asleep."

"Then I am not I," said Trina gaily. So she went to the village and didn't come back and Hans no longer had Trina as hired girl.

Germany

The Transformed Donkey

Three or four mischievous Oxford scholars, walking one day near Abingdon, saw a man asleep in a ditch, holding by the bridle a donkey loaded with earthen crockery.

"Help me," said one to the rest, "and I'll get us a little money! We'll sell this donkey at Abingdon Fair. Shift the donkey's baskets onto my back and put the bridle over my head. Then lead the donkey away and sell it, and leave me with the old man."

This was done and in a little while the man awoke and was surprised to see his donkey thus changed.

"Oh!" pleaded the scholar, "take this bridle out of my mouth and this load from my back!"

"Heavens! how came you here?" asked the astonished old man.

"Why," said the scholar, "my father is a great magician, and at something I did which displeased him he turned me into a donkey. But now his heart has relented and I have returned to my own shape again. I beg you to let me go home and thank him."

"By all means," said the crockery merchant. "I want nothing to do with conjuration!" So he set the scholar at liberty, who went directly to his fellows. By this time they were making merry with the money they had sold the donkey for.

The next day the old man went to the fair to look for a new donkey, and after he had seen several others, he saw his own. It was shown to him as a very good one.

"Oh, no!" said he. "Have he and his father quarreled again already! No, no, I'll have nothing to do with him."

England

Tying Up the Stones

A countryman, who had never been in a city or seen a paved street came to London. He was walking along when suddenly a dog came out of a house and ran furiously at him. The man stooped down to pick up a stone to throw at the dog but found all the stones fixed tight in the cobble-stone paving. "What a strange country I am in," said the man, "where the people tie up the stones and let the dogs loose."

England

Frozen Music

There was once a very cold winter. A coachman driving down a deep narrow ravine in the Black Forest saw a wagon coming toward him. He took up his carriage horn to signal to the other driver to stop and let the coach pass out of the ravine. But however hard the coachman blew, he could not get a single note to come out of his horn. Meanwhile the wagon kept coming ever deeper into the ravine, and since neither could pass by the other the coachman simply drove his coach over the wagon and went on his way.

But in order not to have the same inconvenience happen again, he again lifted up his horn and started blowing. He blew all the songs he knew into it, for he thought the horn was frozen and that he could thaw it out with his warm breath. But what he did didn't help. It was so cold that not a note came out. At last, about nightfall, he came to the town where horses and drivers were to be replaced, stopped at the inn where he regularly stopped, and ordered a glass of wine to help him warm up. Since the regular tavern room was being used for a wedding, he took his wine into the kitchen, hung his horn on a nail on the wall, sat down by the warm stove, and started talking to the cook.

All of a sudden, however, he had a real fright when his carriage horn started blowing by itself. At first it blew several times the signal he had given for the wagon to get out of his way. Then all the songs he had blown into it started coming out. They had frozen fast when he blew them in, and as they thawed out on the warm wall they came out one after the other. There were love songs and funny songs and at last came a fine hymn, "Now all the woods are tranquil." It was the last song the coachman had blown into the horn.

Germany

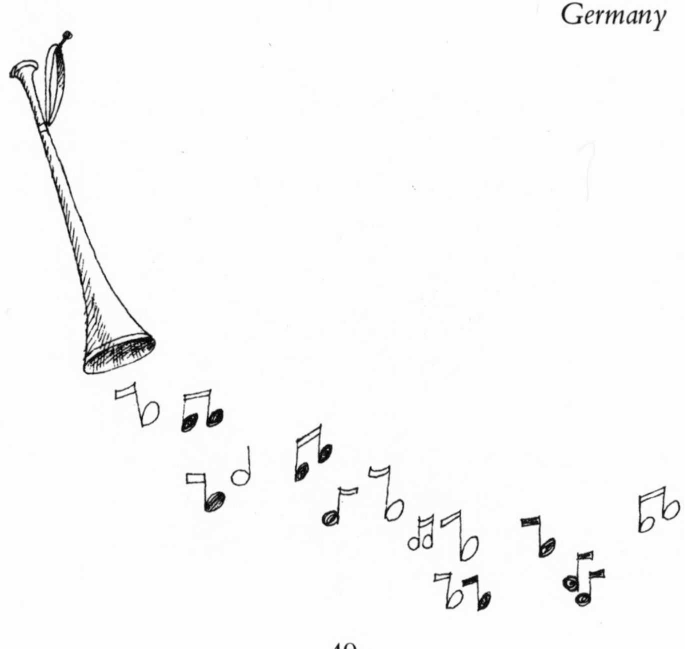

Are Fish Buffaloes?

Three simpletons, roving together in a jungle, came to a lake full of beautiful fish. One of them said, "Oh, these poor fish! How would they survive if the lake should suddenly catch fire and start burning?"

The second replied, "That would be no problem for them! If such a disaster came, the fish would simply climb up in the trees and escape the fire."

The third said scornfully, "Do you think that fish are buffaloes, who can climb trees?"

After these observations the three foolish ones continued their roving through the jungle.

India

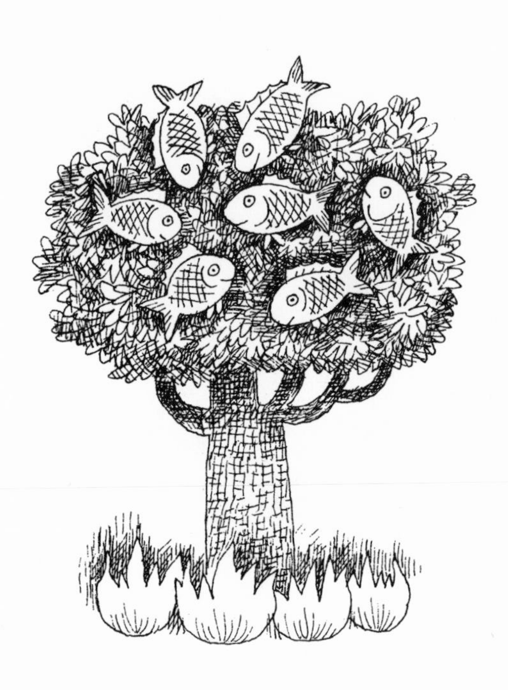

The Clever Boy

There was a man who could tell bigger stories than anyone else. One day he went out with his cow and said he would give her to anyone who could beat him at story telling. He went round among the neighbors, but none of them could win against him. Late that night he came to a hut where he found a little boy asleep. He asked the boy for a coal to light up his pipe. The boy started to shake the fire up and down, and the man got tired waiting.

"Little boy, what are you doing with that fire?" he asked impatiently.

"I am separating today's fire from yesterday's, and yesterday's from day before yesterday's, to give you the hottest coal," said the boy.

"Little boy, give me some water," the man said.

"All right," answered the boy. He began to shake the water jar up and down, until the man got tired waiting.

"Why don't you give me the water?" he asked.

"I am separating today's water from yesterday's, and yesterday's from day before yesterday's, to give you the freshest water," said the boy.

"Have you a mother?" asked the man.

"Yes, sir," said the boy.

"Where is she?"

"She has gone with her needle and thread to sew up a hole in the king's palace that the wind tore in it last night."

"What!" said the man. "And where is your father?"

"He has taken a pot with a hole in it to the river to get water to throw on the land to make a garden."

"Little boy," said the man, "did you hear that a child was born last night, with seven arms and seven necks?"

"No, sir," said the boy, "but this morning when I went to the spring for water, I saw a shirt on the line with seven

sleeves and seven collars. I think it must have belonged to that baby."

"Little boy," said the man, "did you hear that last week a donkey took a trip into the sky?"

"No, sir," said the boy, "but last week when I went to the spring for water, I heard a clap of thunder, and when I looked up I saw a packsaddle falling down from the sky. I think it must have belonged to that mule."

"Little boy," said the man, "did you hear that the river caught fire last week?"

"No, sir," said the boy, "but when I went fishing last week I caught a lot of fish burnt on one side and raw on the other. I think they must have been cooked when the river caught fire."

"Take my cow, little boy," said the man. "You are the cleverest fellow I ever saw."

Portugal

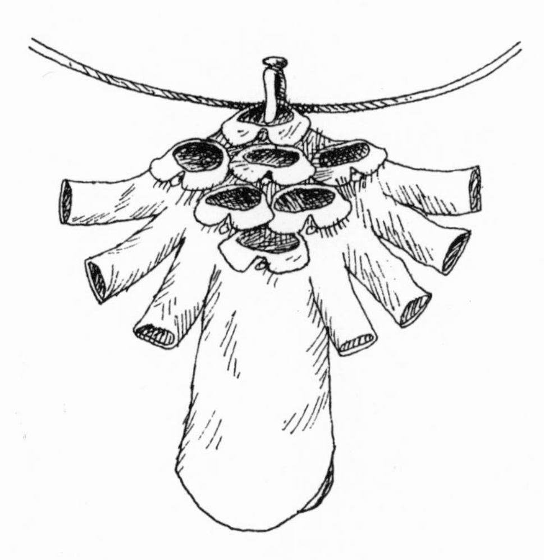

The Three Brothers

Once there was a man who had three sons and nothing else but the house he lived in. Now each son wanted to have the house after his father's death, but the father loved them all alike and did not know what to do. He did not want to sell the house and divide the money among them, because the house had come down from his forefathers.

At last a plan came to him and he said to his sons, "Go out into the world, and each of you learn a trade. When you come back, the one who performs the greatest feat shall have the house."

The sons were happy with this, and the eldest decided to become a blacksmith, the second a barber and the third a fencing master. They named a time when they would come home again, and all set forth.

It happened that each found a skillful teacher and learned his trade well. The blacksmith had to shoe the king's horses and thought, "I shall without fail win the house." The barber shaved only lords and other fine people and thought the house would surely be his. The fencing master suffered many a blow, but he gritted his teeth and let nothing trouble him. He said to himself, "If you are afraid of a blow you'll never win the house."

When the time they had set came around, they came together again at their father's house. But since they did not know how to find the best opportunity to show their skills, they sat down to consult together. As they were sitting there, a hare came running across the field.

"Ah," said the barber, "here he comes, just as if I had

called him!" He took basin and soap and worked up a lather while the hare drew near. Then he soaped and shaved off the hare's whiskers while he was in full flight, without cutting him or injuring a single hair.

"That's well done!" said the father. "If the others don't do something better, the house is yours."

It wasn't long until a nobleman came dashing up at full speed in his coach. "Now you shall see what I can do, father," said the blacksmith. He sprang after the coach, took all four shoes off one of the horses and nailed four new shoes on him as he galloped along.

"You are really a clever fellow," said the father. "You do your task as well as your brother. I really don't know which one I ought to give the house to."

The third son said, "Father, let me have my turn, too." Just then it began to rain, and he drew out his fencing sword and brandished it back and forth over his head so fast that not a drop fell on him. It rained harder and harder until at last it came down in torrents. But he brandished his sword faster and faster and kept as dry as if he were sitting under a roof.

When his father saw this he was amazed and said, "What you have done is the masterpiece! The house is yours."

Both the brothers were satisfied with this, as they had agreed before, and as they all loved one another very much they stayed together in the house and followed their trades. Since they had learned them so well and were so skillful, they earned a lot of money.

Germany

The Boy Who Turned Himself into a Peanut

There was once a boy who thought he could outwit his father. One day he said to his father, "I am going to hide, and you won't be able to find me."

"Hide wherever you like," replied the father. Then he went into his house to rest.

The boy saw a peanut with three kernels and he transformed himself into one of the kernels inside the peanut.

Soon a rooster came along and swallowed the peanut. Then a wild bush cat caught the rooster and swallowed him. Then a dog saw the bush cat, which he chased, caught, and swallowed. A little while later a python swallowed the dog, and then the python went down to the river and was snared in a fish trap.

The father had searched everywhere for his son and, not finding him, he decided to look at his fish trap. When he pulled it up on the bank he found a large python caught in it. He opened up the python and found the dog. He opened the dog and found the bush cat. He opened the bush cat and found the rooster. He opened the rooster and found the peanut. When he broke open the peanut shell, his son stood up!

The boy was so astonished that his father had been able to find him that he never tried again to outwit his father.

Africa: Congo

Improbable Tales from Africa

1. LONG MEMORIES

A man and his brother were on the way to sow their millet. The younger brother went on ahead, carrying the millet seed on his head.

As they walked along, the younger brother suddenly stopped and said, "It is sweet!"

They sowed their millet, cultivated it, harvested it, and then passed a season until the rains came again.

One day the man and his brother started out again to sow their millet.

When they came to the same place where the younger brother had spoken the year before, the older brother asked, "What is sweet?"

The younger brother answered, "Honey!"

Now which of the two brothers had the best memory?

2. THREE SKILLFUL MEN

A man with good ears, one who could count fast, and one with good eyes, were sailing across a river in a canoe. They had a basket full of grain.

The wind blew; a seed fell into the water. The man with good ears said, "Oh! I heard a seed fall into the water."

The fast counter counted the grain seeds in the basket in an instant and said, "That's true. One is missing."

The man with good eyes plunged to the bottom of the river and picked that seed up from the sand.

All the while, the canoe was sailing along.

Which of the three was most skillful?

3. TWO SPEEDY PEOPLE

A man and his younger brother were going to a field to plant millet, and the younger brother carried the basket of seed on his head. A heavy rain had fallen the night before and the younger brother slipped in the mud and fell. Before hitting the ground he had time enough to set the basket down, take off his white robe and trousers, and put on some old clothes.

When they got to the field they sat down under a tree, and an antelope ran by. The older brother took up his gun and shot at it. Then he ran to the antelope, killed it with his knife, skinned it, packed the meat in the skin, and slung the pack on his shoulder. Just then the bullet arrived. He grabbed it in flight and said, "Don't ruin my meat!"

Which of the two was speediest?

4. FOUR VERY SKILLFUL PEOPLE

A young man was chased from home by his father because he could see too well. Another was chased away by his father because he was too deft. A third was chased away by his father because he was too strong. The three men met in a road and each told the other why he was sent from home. They said, "Let us travel together." So they started toward a village.

The man who could see well looked up into the sky and saw a horse tied to a cloud. The deft man shot an arrow which cut the horse's bonds. When the horse fell, the strong man stopped its fall with his hands, but he was so strong that the horse bounced up from his hands and fell into the village.

The three men ran lickety-split toward the village to catch the horse. They met an old woman who was carrying its bones to the refuse heap. The old woman had had time to catch the horse, kill it, cook it, eat it, gather up the bones and carry them out of the village.

Which of the four had the greatest skill?

5. THE THREE GLUTTONS AND THE HUNTER

Three men were chased away from their homes by their fathers because each was a glutton. The father of each gave his son a basket full of beans to eat along the way. The three men met on a road beneath a large baobab tree.

The eldest questioned the others, and both explained that they had been sent from home because they ate too much. The eldest said, "Then we are all alike!" They put a big pot on a fire and poured the three baskets of beans into it.

They took the beans off the fire when they were barely cooked, because they did not want to wait any longer. Now they were worried about how to eat them, because if they used their hands one would get more than the others.

The eldest said, "Let us each take a needle and pick the beans out of the pot one by one with the needle. We will all put our hands into the pot at the same time and take them out at the same time."

They began eating the beans one by one, and they ate until only one bean was left in the pot. Each wanted it and they almost came to blows quarreling about who was to get it.

A hunter heard them shouting and came and asked them the cause of their quarrel. They told him, and the hunter said, "Do you want me to decide it for you?"

They agreed to this.

The hunter pulled out his sword and cut the bean in three parts. Each one ate his share.

Then the hunter licked the sword with his tongue to get the taste of the bit of bean that was there.

Which of these four men was the biggest glutton?

Africa: Mali

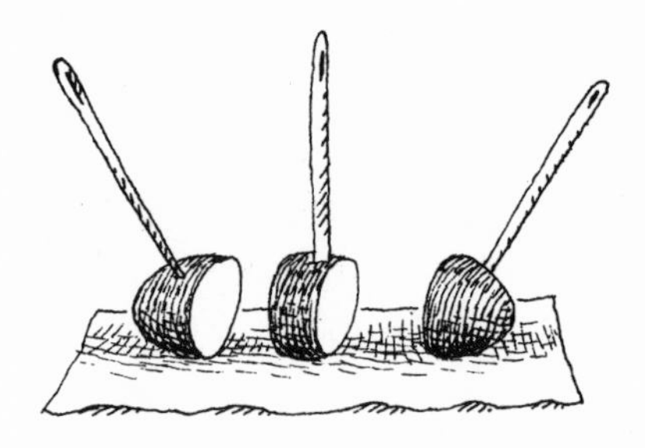

The Louse Skin Drum

Well, there was a very powerful king who had a big palace where he and his daughter lived. One day when he was combing his hair he found a louse. Since he was a very good-humored man he decided to keep the louse and watch it grow. So he had a little box made for it to live in. He fed it every day and it grew so fast that the box was soon too small for it.

So the king killed the louse, dried its skin and made a little drum. He made the drumhead, or face, from the louse skin, and had the drum base made from a stalk of fennel. Then he announced publicly that whoever could guess what the little drum was made of could marry the princess.

A lot of people came to see the drum, but nobody could guess what it was made of. At last a young shepherd came to the palace bringing with him a very well brought up

little mouse that he had taken away from a cat. The mouse crept into the room where the little drum was kept, and he smelled and he smelled until he knew what it was made of. Then he returned to the shepherd and said to him:

> Fennel base;
> Louse skin face.

So now the shepherd asked to see the drum. He took it in his hands, he looked at it, he felt it, and at last he smelt it. Then he said:

> Ladies and gentlemen!
> Fennel base;
> Louse skin face.

The princess married the shepherd and they were very happy. The little mouse continued to live with them and did them many favors.

Puerto Rico

The Shadow

One bright moonlit night, the three foolish brothers of Bakki were traveling across ice. One was riding their black mare while the others walked. Suddenly they noticed that a man rode at the side of the rider, imitating him in every movement. The oddest thing was that he spoke not a word, except that they heard him say, at each step the mare took, something like, "Clop, Clop!" They found this the more odd, since none of them was named Clop. The rider decided to ride on fast and leave this fellow behind. But the faster he rode, the oftener and louder he heard, "Clop, Clop!" and the others saw that the man stayed right at his side, whether he rode fast or slow. At last they got home, and they saw the rider dismount at the same time as their brother, and take his horse into the stable at the same time their brother led in the black mare. But when they got into the stable out of the moonlight, the strange rider had disappeared utterly from their eyes!

Iceland

The Remarkable Ox, Rooster, and Dog

One day a man noted for his exaggerated stories told a friend that he had at home three extraordinary and precious things: an ox that could travel a thousand *li* (over three hundred miles) a day, a rooster that crowed at the beginning of every hour, day and night, and a dog that could read books. The friend said that he expected to lose no time in seeing such marvels with his own eyes. He promised to go the very next day.

The man did not expect this, as his home was somewhat distant, and he went home quite unhappily. He told his wife that he had at last got caught in his stories, and that he would be disgraced tomorrow when the friend arrived.

"Never mind," said the wife. "Leave things up to me and everything will be all right. Only you must keep out of sight."

The next morning the visitor arrived and was met by the wife. He asked to see her husband.

"He is not here," she replied. "He has gone to Peking."

"When will he be back?"

"In four or five days," she said.

"Why, how can he return so quickly?" he asked.

"Oh, he went off this morning on our fast ox and can do it easily," she said.

"I hear that you also have a wonderful rooster," said the visitor—and by luck, just as he spoke, the rooster crowed.

"That is he," said the wife. "He crows at the beginning of each hour and he also crows whenever a visitor comes."

"I would also like to see your learned dog," he said.

"Ah," she said, "I am sorry. But you see we are very poor, so he keeps a school in the city."

China

Little Chinese Tales

1. THE STOLEN ROPE

A man was caught for stealing a cow and put in the pillory. Some friends came by and, seeing him there, asked what he had done.

"Oh, nothing," he said. "I merely saw a piece of old rope on the road and picked it up."

"Surely you would not receive so severe a punishment for picking up a piece of useless rope."

"Well," said the man, "there was a small cow on the end of it."

2. THE HIDDEN HOE

A man was at work in the fields when his wife called to him, "Come in to dinner!"

"All right!" he shouted. "Just wait till I have hidden my hoe!"

When he got in, his wife reproved him. "You should hide your hoe secretly," she said. "To shout out as you did is the surest way to get it stolen."

He was so struck by her remark that he returned at once to the field. Sure enough the hoe was gone. He hurried back to the house and whispered very softly into his wife's ear, "Someone has stolen it."

3. THE MAN IN THE MIRROR

Once there was a man who was very poor and so deeply in debt that he saw no way to improve his situation. So he set out into the world, and when he was crossing a desert he found a box full of jewels. The lid of the box had a mirror attached to the underside.

When the man lifted the lid and saw the jewels he was very happy. Then he opened the lid wide, saw a man in the mirror, and was greatly frightened. He joined his hands together in supplication and said, "Oh, sir, I thought that this box was completely empty. I didn't know, sir, that you were inside it. Please don't be angry at me."

China

The King and the Wrestler

A wrestler once approached the King of Malabar and said, "I have all the arts of combat and can fight with wild animals, and I can even walk with a large mountain on my head. But I have found no one able to give me the wages due my powers. So I have come into your presence in the hope that you will give me a suitable livelihood." The king hired him at a high wage, thinking that such a warrior would be very serviceable to him.

There was a huge mountain near the king's city infested with wild beasts which were causing much havoc among the people. One day the king sent for the warrior and said, "You declared, you know, that you could carry a mountain on your shoulders. There is a mountain in the neighborhood where animals live that are causing much suffering among the people. Take it away to a distant spot and return here."

The wrestler promised obedience, and the next day at dawn the king, with his ministers, priests, and a retinue of soldiers, took him to the foot of the mountain. The wrestler girded up his waistband, tied his turban, and stood ready. After some time the king said to him, "Why are you waiting? Take the mountain on your head and go!"

The wrestler replied, "Sir, I humbly told you that I could carry the mountain on my head. I did not say that I could lift it up there. Kindly command your soldiers to tear the mountain up and place it on my head and I will carry it to whatever place you may command me."

India

The Age of the Animals

In the realm of a king lived an elephant, an ape, a hare, and a snowfowl. They decided to bestow honor on the oldest among them, and agreed to announce this honor to all members of his tribe. But who was the oldest? They didn't know how to reckon time in years. Nearby stood a great oak tree.

The elephant said: "When I was born, this tree was just my height. I am the age of this tree."

The ape answered: "Then I am older. When I was born this tree was not so tall as I. As a boy I sprang over its roots."

Then spoke the hare: "When I was born, the tree was even smaller than I. I drank the dew from its leaves."

Now the snowfowl spoke: "I am still older than you all. I carried here in my beak the seed-acorn of this tree. The tree grew up here from that acorn."

So the creatures are ranked today. The elephant is youngest and carries the ape on his back. The ape carries the hare. The hare carries the snowfowl.

Tibet

Who Am I?

A poor man who had passed all his life in forests resolved to try his fortune in a great city, and as he drew near it he observed with wonder the crowds on the road. He thought, "I shall certainly not be able to know myself among so many people if I have not something about me that the others have not." So he tied a pumpkin to his right leg and, thus decorated, entered the town.

A young wag, perceiving the simpleton, made friends with him, and induced him to spend the night at his house.

While he was asleep, the joker removed the pumpkin from his leg and tied it to his own, and then lay down again.

In the morning, when the poor fellow awoke and found the pumpkin on his companion's leg, he called to him, "Hey! get up, for I am perplexed in my mind. Who am I, and who are you? If I am I, why is the pumpkin on your leg? And if you are you, why is the pumpkin not on my leg?"

Persia

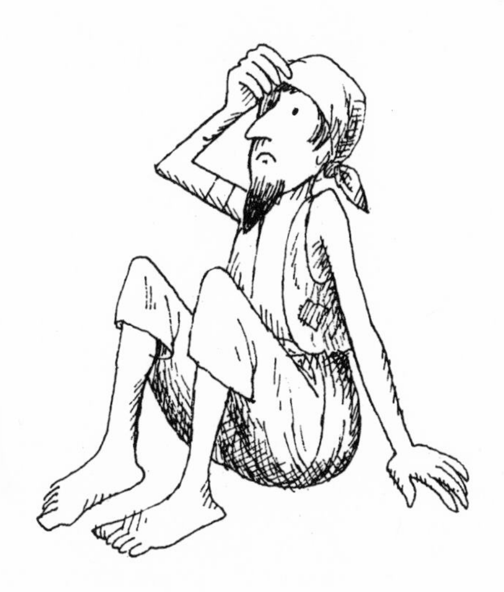

Little Tall Tales

1. SNAKE STORY

Two snakes found an egg and started quarreling over it. Somehow each got hold of the other's tail and began to swallow. They swallowed and swallowed until at last there was nothing at all left except the egg over which they had quarreled.

2. THE POPCORN FROST

A farmer once planted a big field of popcorn. In late summer, when the popcorn was ripe, there came a day so hot that the popcorn started popping. A horse in the next field thought it was snow and froze to death.

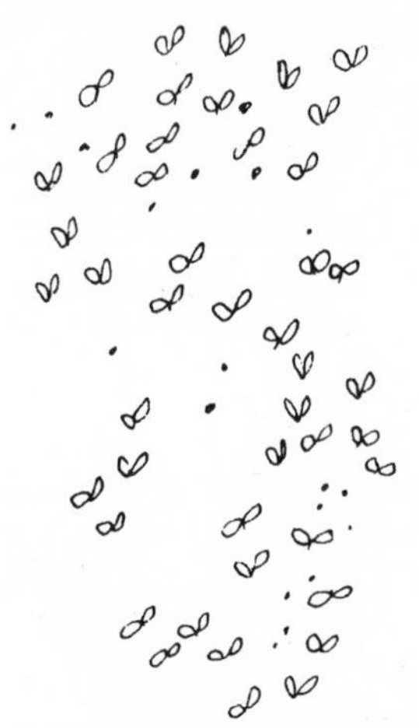

3. THE FLYING KETTLE

Once a swarm of mosquitoes started chasing a man, who took refuge from them under a big iron kettle. The mosquitoes drove their stingers through the kettle and the man clinched them all with a hammer as they came through. Soon the mosquitoes soared away, taking the iron kettle with them.

4. SHINGLING THE FOG

A man was shingling his house and a thick fog came up. He wanted to finish the job and went right on with his work. When the fog lifted he found that he had shingled six feet beyond the edge of his roof.

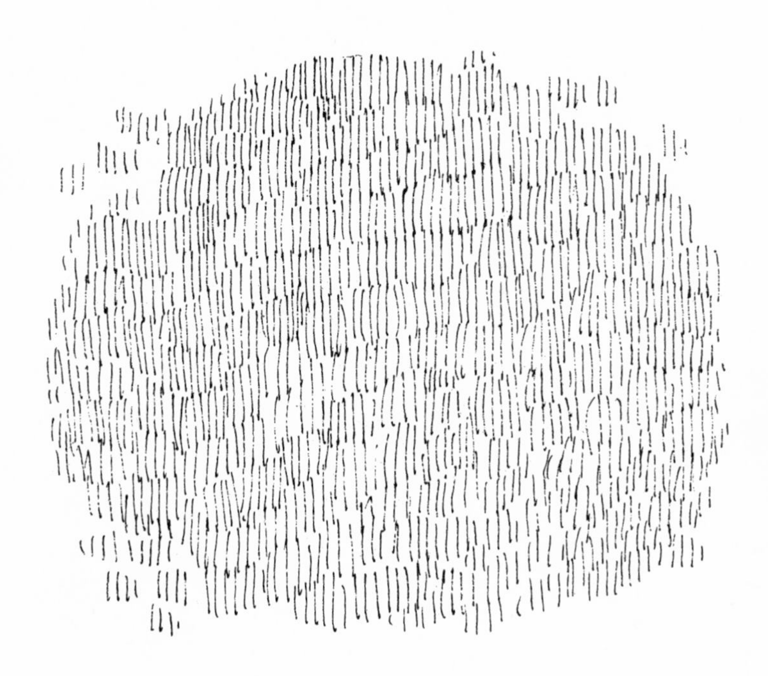

5. GREAT HUNTING!

A hunter with one bullet in his gun was standing on a riverbank and saw six turkeys on a limb and a deer standing nearby. He fired so that his bullet split the limb, glanced off it, and hit the deer. The split limb closed up

Sing Something

Once a fool lost his way in going from one village to another and asked someone how to get there.

"Follow this path up around the tree on the river bank," he was told.

He came to the tree and started climbing it, up and up and round and round. At last he came out onto a bough which bent down low, to which he hung clinging by his hands. By and by an elephant driver came by to water his animal.

The fool said, "Great sir, take me down!"

The elephant driver reached up to lift him down, and in doing so dropped his elephant hook. The elephant went on, leaving the driver hanging to the fool's feet.

The fool said, "Sing out, so that people will come and take us down. Otherwise we shall fall, and the river will carry us away."

The elephant driver started to sing, and he sang so sweetly that the fool let go of his bough to applaud. And so both fell into the water.

India

Big, Big Lies!

Once I was lying in my father's attic looking up into the weather and I saw a tiny land hanging up there on four white handles and it was full of fish pudding. I was always very fond of fish pudding and now one fell down to me and ran round and round until it ran into a wheel, when it turned into a youth. I christened him Jeppe. He didn't want to stay with me; he wanted to go back to that tiny land, but he went to the king's court and asked to be the king's huntsman. "No," said the king, "I have a huntsman!" But Jeppe insisted so much that the king said, "Well, so now I have two huntsmen! The one who goes out tomorrow morning and brings home the most game shall marry my daughter."

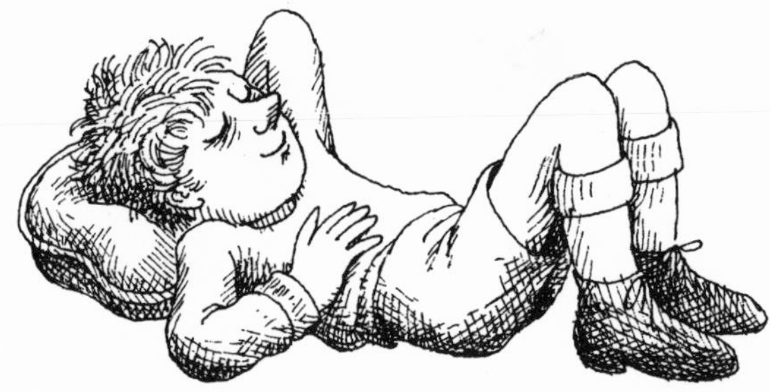

The other huntsman was old; he got up long before day, loaded his gun, put food into his pocket, and went to the forest. Jeppe lay abed late. The king's daughter much preferred Jeppe, who was young and lively. She went to him and said, "Jep, Jep! get up. Don't you remember what my father said last night?"

"Yes, yes," said Jep. "There's plenty of time." Then he got up, ate his breakfast, loaded his gun, put food in his pocket, and went to the forest.

Soon he came across the older huntsman, who hadn't even shot a fly. "Can you show me where the game is?" he asked Jeppe. Jeppe said, "Sure!" and showed him a path where no game had ever been since the world began.

Jep went on a little way and found a swarm of bees, which he put into his pocket. A little way further he shot a gray goose, and as he bent over to pick it up he fell over

a wild duck with fifty ducklings. Then he shot a lot more gray geese, swans, hares, foxes, deer, and all sorts of things, till he had a whole wagon full.

But how was he to get his game home? He decided to find a forester's dwelling and borrow a horse and wagon to haul it. A short distance on, he saw four wheels running along. They were headed for the moor to gather berries. He asked if they would help him carry his game home. "Yes," they said. "We can gather berries another day."

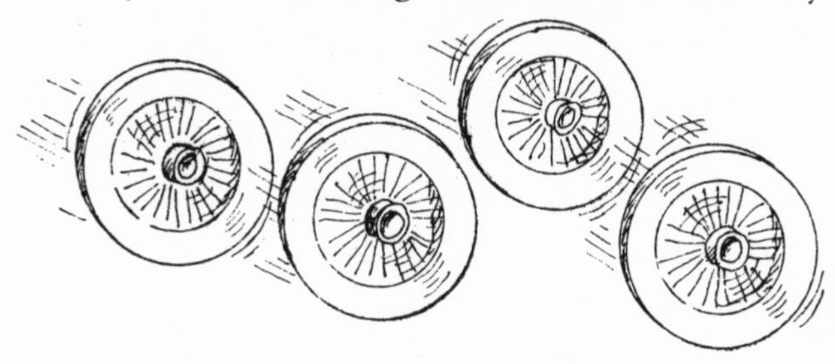

He went a bit further and saw four wagonbed planks striking each other and a fifth plank trying to stop the fight. He asked if they would help him carry his game home and they said, "Yes, we can fight another day!"

A little further he found a wagon tongue, a doubletree, and two singletrees and they were all willing to help him get his game home. So now he had everything to put a wagon together; he lacked only a team to draw it. So he pulled up a couple of roots from the ground and made a pair of crows with them. He made tugs out of the bark and hitched the crows to the wagon, but they couldn't

pull it. So now he hitched himself up instead, and *he* pulled it.

When he got home the other huntsman was already there. He hadn't even caught a bee, and the king was so angry that when the kitchen maid came out and asked for firewood, he split it with his nose.

The king tried to get out of his promise, but Jep said he thought a man's word was his word and that the king should live up to his word. The king answered that nobody should ever say he was a man who broke his word, but there was just one thing more he wanted Jep to do. He should take a walk with the king's daughter, and if he could make her say, "You lie in your throat," then he could have her. The king had strongly forbidden her to say these words.

So now they went walking in the garden. She said, "These are tall cabbage heads that my father has!"

"Oh, not so tall," said Jep. "My father's cabbage heads are a lot taller. Ten mounted horsemen can stand one on top of the other and still not reach the top of a cabbage. That's what *I* call big cabbage heads."

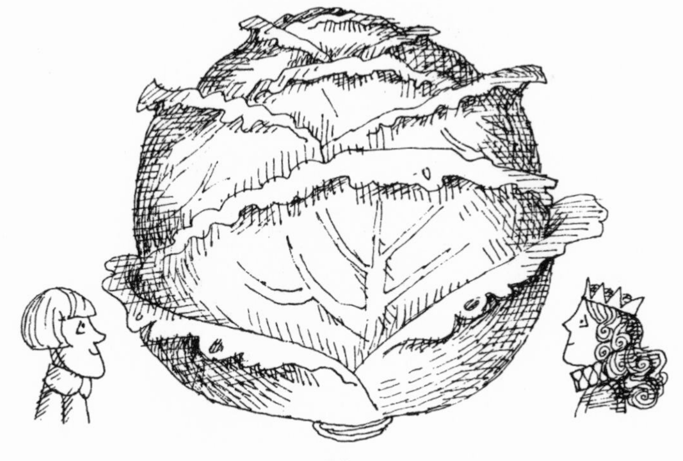

She still insisted, however, that her father's cabbage heads were bigger.

"Why," he said, "they are nothing compared to my father's. One grew so big that a king and all his cavalry could shelter under a single leaf. One time a knight drew his sword and cut a hole in a leaf, and all the knights fell in and drowned, except for me."

She said, "That may very well be true."

They walked further and came to the beehives.

"These are big bees my father has," she said.

"Oh, not so big," he replied. "My father's bees are much bigger. They are as big as your geese here."

"How do they get into the beehives?" she asked.

"Oh, that is something they know how to do!" he said.

She answered, "That may very well be true."

They walked further: there went the geese with their goslings.

"These geese of my father's are very big," she said.

"*They* aren't big," he said. "My father's geese are much bigger. Once when we wanted to make an egg cake from one egg, we had to use all our axes and hammers, just to break it. And when it was broken we had to use all our warships to put the egg into the pan. Otherwise the whole land would have been inundated with egg."

"That may very well be true," she said.

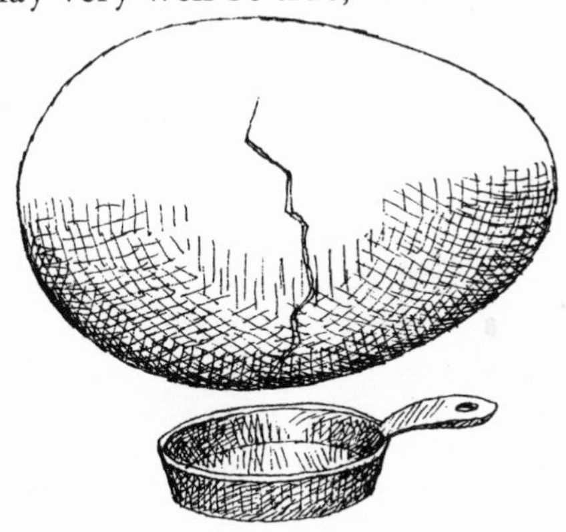

Now they were tired of the garden and walked to the stable.

"My father has a fine high stable," she said.

"It's not so high," he said. "My father's is much higher. Once when a roofer sat high up on the roof and dropped a roofing nail, a magpie came, built her nests, laid her eggs, and hatched out three broods of young before the nail hit the ground—and the nail was falling all that time."

"That may very well be true," she said.

They walked inside the stable.

"This is a fine long stall my father has," she said.

"It's not so long," he said. "My father has a stall much longer. It is so long that a cow, standing with her little calf on one side of the stall, would have a second calf before the stable boy could fetch hay for the first calf from the other side of the stall."

"That may very well be true," she said.

She said, "My father has many, many cows."

"Not so many," he said. "My father has many more. We had a valley where we milked them, called Long Valley, and we had an old gray mare we called Longcrab. She and several other horses used to tread the curds when we made cheese. We would tie rennet onto the feet of geese and let them swim through the milk to curdle it.

One day when the old gray mare and the other horses were treading the milk, they sank down in the cheese and got lost. A long time afterwards my mother sent me to town on an errand and gave me a piece of bread and cheese to eat on the way. When I got hungry and took the bread and cheese out of my pocket and started eating it, I found Longcrab and eleven other horses inside it. In those days I was strong and could carry a lot, and my pocket was big then, too."

"That may very well be true," she said.

"So now I didn't have to walk. I climbed up on Longcrab, but when I had ridden a short distance, her backbone broke. I had a hazel stick in my hand, and I made her a new backbone out of that. I got on again and rode a short way further, and a great hazel forest full of nuts grew out of that hazel stick. I climbed up and began to gather nuts.

"When I got to the top, I saw the good Lord and St. Peter. They were cradling oats and the holy Mary was separating the chaff from the grain. I climbed off and watched them awhile, but when I wanted to come down again, my hazelwood forest had disappeared. So I took some of the chaff and twisted me a rope. It didn't quite reach the earth. I tied a hen's egg to the end of it, but it still didn't reach. So then I scrounged around in my pocket to see what I had there and found a little whetstone, which I stretched out three hundred seventy three yards long and added it to the rope. That helped. To get down the rest of the way, I jumped ten yards, and landed on the tail of a fox where a straw barley preacher was reading the harvest mass. And there were your father and mine going to make an offering."

"That may very well be true," she said.

"My father had a silver penny for the offering and your father had none. So my father broke his silver penny in two and gave half to your father."

"That may very well be true."

"My father took off his hat, as he made his offering, but your father wouldn't take his off."

"Why not?" she asked. "I have never known him to be so impolite."

"That happened," he said, "because my father's head was clean and your father's head was scabby."

"You lie in your throat!" she cried.

"That's what I've tried to get you to say for a long time," he said.

Now they went to the king and explained things, and while they stood before him and told him the whole story, I sat in a mousehole behind the door and listened.

The wedding was soon celebrated and the rejoicing and noise were beyond description. Suddenly they found themselves without gunwadding and started looking for it behind all the doors, and they found me sitting in my mousehole, and they grabbed me and stuffed me into a cannon and shot me clear here, so that I could sit here and tell all these big lies.

Denmark

The Story Without an End

There was a raja of a certain country who asked no question of the learned men who came to his court but, "Do you know a story?" After they had told him all the tales they knew, he would say contemptuously, "Don't you know any more tales than these? You may go."

One learned man, when he heard how the raja dismissed all comers, went to him.

"What is your name?" the raja asked him.

"I am called 'Sea-of-Stories,' " the man answered.

"Then how many stories do you know?" the raja asked.

"There is no end to my tales," he said. "That is why I have my name."

"Tell me a tale," said the raja.

The man began: "In a royal lake ten thousand miles long and five thousand miles wide, there grew lotus flowers upon which a hundred billion golden-winged swans alighted. Once there came up a furious wind and rain, and to escape the storm all those swans flew into a mountain cavern for shelter."

A Word About this Book

In A WORLD OF NONSENSE I have brought together about fifty of the most amusing nonsense stories I could find in reading several thousand folktales from many lands. My purpose has been to assemble stories which share a humorous and sometimes very strange quality of exaggeration. All leap, at some point or other, from the everyday world of reality into an impossible, absurd, and utterly delightful world of nonsense. This is quite a different world from the magical one of supernatural happenings that we enter when we read fairy tales, though it is equally far from the real world about us (however "nonsensical," in another sense, the latter may sometimes seem). When we read the stories of Cinderella, or of the twelve brothers who were turned into ravens, or of Sindbad the sailor, we must read them seriously and with momentary belief (or at least "suspension of disbelief") if we are to come under their spell. The enchantment of the present stories is of another kind: it is their complete impossibility and absurdity which captivate us. The pleasure of hearing or reading them lies specifically in their incredibility. No one "believes" them for a moment, nor would anyone ever regret (as a child sometimes may with fairy tales) that the real world is so workaday or "commonplace" in comparison.

While most of the stories in this book will be unfamiliar to young readers, the types of folktales that they represent are very well known to folklorists. A majority are what folklorists classify as tall tales ("tales of lying") or as "numskull stories" (stories of numskulls, noodles, fools). The reader wishing to know more about the great variety of such stories and their reported range in the world's folklore should consult Antti Aarne and Stith Thompson, *The Types of the Folktale* (1961). In that book Types 1200-1349 (pp. 374-400) are "numskull stories" and Types 1875-1999 (pp. 509-521) are "tales of lying." Similar information is in Stith Thompson's *Motif-Index of Folk Literature* (6 v., 1955-58), where Motifs J1700-J2799 treat "fools (and other unwise persons)" and Motifs X900-X1899 cover "the humor of lies and exaggerations." A very delightful book that is entirely about numskulls is W. A. Clouston, *The Book of Noodles* (London, 1888); it recounts the imaginary doings of foolish people, as told in many lands over two millennia. A number of types of story other than those described above are also represented in the present book, including some that folklorists classify as tales of magic and the supernatural. They find their place here because the magical or supernatural interventions are, for the most part, so humorously or spoofingly narrated as to suggest the exaggerations of tall tales.

In the following Notes and Comments I have given full sources for all the stories. Most are printed here as received, or with slight verbal or syntactical adaptations for clarity, or are translated with careful adherence to the originals. Some are retold simply for economy, with care not to alter content. In a few cases where I have used only part of an original story or have omitted or altered an episode or significant detail, the changes are indicated in the notes. For a few stories whose range and distribution in world folklore I have considered exceptionally interesting I have given the Aarne-Thompson Type number. A good many additional stories or parts of stories related to those in the text also appear. They are intended to be a small and (I hope) amusing demonstration of how folktales run round the world, often changing in fascinating and illuminating ways as they go from country to country, or from narrator to narrator.

C. W.

Notes and Comments

A WORLD OF NONSENSE, p. 1, from "A Tale of Nonsense," in *North Indian Notes and Queries*, Nov., 1894, 136. Our first story is the formula introduction, complete in itself, to a long and complicated variant of our next story, THE MIGHTY WRESTLERS. "A Tale of Nonsense" continues: "Presently he saw a little girl lift the carcass of the elephant on a straw and ask her mother where she should throw it. 'It is only a little mouse,' said the girl. The man said, 'What power must the father of such a girl possess!' So he asked her where her father was. . . ." A tall tale, slightly adapted.

THE MIGHTY WRESTLERS, p. 2, ("The Wrestlers, a Story of Heroes"), Flora Annie Steel, *Tales of the Punjab (Told by the People)*, Macmillan & Co., London, 1894, 211-15. This tall tale or "lying story," Aarne-Thompson Type 1962A, Great Wrestlers (or big eaters), is very popular in India. In some versions a great bird carries off one rival (or both) and all the animals, dropping them into the eye of a girl who complains that a little sand has fallen into her eye. Slightly adapted.

WHAT NEWS? NEWS ENOUGH! p. 7, J. Fleury, *La Littérature Orale de la Basse-Normandie*. Les Littératures populaires de toutes les nations, XI, Paris, 1883, 208-10. A tall tale, translated from French.

THE SHIP THAT SAILED ON WATER AND ON LAND, p. 9, ("La bbarca"), Giggi Zanazzo, *Novelle, Favole e Leggende Romanesche*, Turin-Rome, 1907, 123-32. Reprinted in standard Italian (with slight additions omitted here) as "La barca che va per mare e per terra" in Italo Calvino, *Fiabe Italiane*, [Turin], 1956, 498-502. A "tale of supernatural helpers" who (except for the little old man who completes the ship magically) sound more like tall tale characters than supernaturals. Type 513B, The Land and Water Ship (related to Grimm No. 71, "How Six Men Got on in the World"). Translated from Italian.

THE DONKEY'S EGG, p. 18, Paul Sébillot, *Les Contes Populaires de la Haute-Bretagne*, 2me. Série. Les Littératures populaires de toutes les nations, I, Paris, 1881, 255. An extremely widespread numskull tale. Type 1319, Pumpkin Sold as an Ass's [or mare's] Egg. Translated from French. In most U.S. versions the donkey's (or mare's) egg is a pumpkin, but in one a gullible youth is given a coconut as a "mule's egg." After sitting on the coconut for weeks he finally gets disgusted and throws it into a weed patch, scaring out a jackrabbit. The boy yells, "Come back here, you fool mule! Don't you know I'm your pappy?" (B. A. Botkin, *American Anecdotes*, Random House, N.Y., 1957, 84-85.)

A TRIP TO THE SKY, p. 19, ("If You Don't Like it, Don't Listen"), A. N. Afanasyev, *Narodnye Russkie Skazki* (Russian Folktales), 3 v., Moscow, 1957, v. III, 229-31. Type 1960G, The Great Tree (plants growing to heaven, etc.). This charming Russian tall tale, with its seven-eyed magical goat, will remind readers of our own magical tale Jack and the Beanstalk. See also BIG, BIG LIES!, p. 90, from Denmark. This story and the next one are edited from translations from Russian by Dr. Sula Benet, New York City.

AIR CASTLES, p. 23, *ibid.*, v. III, 297. A numskull tale of absurd plans and air castles. See various Motifs listed under Type 1430. In American and British versions the daydreamer is usually a girl carrying on her head a pail of milk or basket of eggs which she is going to sell. Imagining her future wealth, greatness and eager suitors, she tosses her head proudly and loses all.

OLD WALL EYES, p. 25, Herbert Halpert Archive, Ray Wood Manuscript, 395-96, contributed by Mrs. Harvey F. Cowart of Pasadena, Texas, "as told for a bedtime story to East Texas children." A humorous "scary" story, adapted by reducing the dialect. The story appears in Ben Botkin and Carl Withers, *Illustrated Book of American Folklore*, Grosset and Dunlap, N.Y., 1958; a somewhat different version is in Vance Randolph, *The Devil's Pretty Daughter*, Columbia University Press, N.Y., 1955.

RIVAL STORYTELLERS, p. 28. Tall tale tellers frequently, as a stylistic device, present their stories in pairs as the competitive tales of "famous" local storytellers, living or of the past. I have heard SEEING FAR AND HEARING FAR, p. 28, only once, from an old man in Wheatland, Mo., in 1940, where I was doing research for my book, James West (pseud.), *Plainville, U.S.A.*, Columbia University Press, N.Y., 1945. (In a French story one man says to his rival, "It was cloudy this morning, and I heard a gnat in wooden shoes clomping round on the church steeple." L. Pineau, *Folk-Lore du Poitou.* Collection de contes et chansons populaires, XVI, Paris, 1898, 83.) THE BIG PUMPKIN AND THE BIG KETTLE, p. 28, and FISH STORY, p. 29, are frequently reported from many regions of the U.S. I heard both repeatedly in Wheatland, Mo., in 1939-40, and the first has been around for several hundred years. (For a seventeenth-century English version see Carl Withers, *I Saw a Rocket Walk a Mile*, Holt, Rinehart and Winston, N.Y., 1965, 71.) I heard THE BOASTFUL ALASKANS, p. 30, orally from an unremembered informant many years ago. All the above stories are retold simply in standard English. THE BIG CHINESE DRUM, p. 30, is retold from a story that appears in several accounts of Chinese humor, including Herbert A. Giles, *Quips from a Chinese Jest-Book*, Shanghai, 1925, 145-46. The same tale with an added storyteller appears in Keigo Seki (Ed.), *Folktales of Japan*, University of Chicago Press, Chicago, 1963. The third man boasts of two trees so tall that their tops are lost from sight in the clouds; they are to be drumsticks for the drum made from the first man's hollow tree (big enough to hold a hundred sleeping mats) and the second man's great cowhide. TRAVELING TO SEE WONDERS, p. 31, Giles, *op. cit.,* 146, retold. A SHILLING FOR A LIE, p. 32, is slightly adapted from a story told by a thirteen-year-old schoolboy, in Elsie Clews Parsons, *Folklore from the Antilles, French and English,* Memoir, American Folklore Society, v. 26, Part I, N.Y., 1933, 93.

THE GREATEST BOAST, p. 33, Albert Wesselski, *Märchen des Mittelalters,* Berlin, 1925, 61. Wesselski repeats the story from a fifteenth-century book of *exempla* used by preachers in their sermons. My first paragraph omits most of a long introduction. Translated from German.

THE PUGILIST AND HIS WONDERFUL HELPERS, p. 35, ("Eine Lüge so gross es nur eine geben kann"), Johannes Bolte and Georg Polívka, *Anmerkungen zu den Kinder- und Hausmärchen der Brüder Grimm*, 5 v., Leipzig, 1912-32, v. II, 80-83. Bolte and Polívka give the story as a "not badly told variant" of Grimm No. 71 ("How Six Men Got on in the World") which was printed in *Vade Mecum für Lustige Leute*, Berlin, 1783. Translated from German.

HANS HANSEN'S HIRED GIRL, p. 43, *ibid.*, v. I, 335, from the 1812 edition of Grimms' tales. It was replaced in later editions by No. 34, "Clever Elsie." Translated from German. See also WHO AM I? p. 80. Numskull stories of people unable to tell their identity are widespread and extremely varied. In "Plainville" the story was often told of a German farmer, long dead and gone, that one day on the road home from town his horses got frightened, turned the wagon over, broke loose and ran away, leaving him unconscious in the road. When he came to, he said, "Who am I? If I'm Henry Helm, I've lost a good team; if I'm not, I've found a wagon."

THE TRANSFORMED DONKEY, p. 45, *Joe Miller's Jests, or the Wit's Vade-Mecum*, London, 1739 (reprinted in facsmile by Dover Publications, N.Y., 1963), 22-24. A numskull and trickster story, slightly adapted. In an older, Persian version (see Burton's *Book of the Thousand Nights and a Night*, 388th night), the sharper slips into the halter while the donkey is moving and draws up sharp as soon as his accomplice has led it out of sight. Allah had turned him into a donkey, he explains, through the supplications of his mother, whom he had struck for reproving him when he came home drunk. When the donkey-owner's wife hears what happened on the road, she is very sad that a transformed human being has been used as a donkey and offers prayers and alms in expiation. It is always diverting to observe how a story, in passing from one culture to another, changes its cultural dress.

TYING UP THE STONES, p. 47. A numskull story adapted from W. A. Clouston, *The Book of Noodles*, London, 1888, 79. Clouston got the story from *Wit and Mirth*, a collection of popular anecdotes published by John Taylor, the Water Poet, London, 1635.

FROZEN MUSIC, p. 48, ("Das Posthorn"), Paul Zaunert, *Deutsche Märchen seit Grimm*, Eugen Diedericks Verlag, Jena, 1922, 30-31.

This is a particularly pleasing version of Type 1889, Frozen Words (Music) Thaw. Translated from German; some song names in the last paragraph are omitted. See also THE BOASTFUL ALASKANS, p. 30. This type of tall tale has been popular for a long time. In *The Tatler*, No. 254, Nov. 23, 1710, appeared an essay, "Frozen Words," by Joseph Addison—some of the words were questionable and when they thawed out caused embarrassment. In December, 1966, a friend in Washington, D.C., told me a frozen flame story from his childhood in Gloucester Co., Va.: A neighbor said it had gotten so cold at his house that the flame in his lamp froze. He threw the lamp outdoors, and a hen ate the frozen flame and laid hard-boiled eggs for three weeks.

ARE FISH BUFFALOES? p. 50, ("The Three Fools"), Rev. Sherman Oakley and Tata Dutt Gairola, *Himalaya Folklore*, Allahabad, U.P., 1935, 191. An Indian numskull story, adapted.

THE CLEVER BOY, p. 51, ("The Biggest Liar. . . ."), Elsie Clews Parsons, *Folk-Lore from the Cape Verde Islands*, Memoir, American Folklore Society, v. 15, Pt. I, 1923, 320-21. This is the slightly adapted first part of a much longer folktale told by a Portuguese woman in New England. In the sequel a wolf told the man, "I'll get the cow back for you. I have seven bags full of lies." But the boy so frightened the wolf with further stories that the wolf leaped off a mountain and died.

THE THREE BROTHERS, p. 55, Grimms' Household Tales, no. 124. Type 654. A tale of "supernatural power or knowledge" which to the modern reader has the humorous effect of a tall tale. I have omitted a few tiresome lines at the end about the long life, death and burial "in the same grave" of the three brothers.

THE BOY WHO TURNED HIMSELF INTO A PEANUT, p. 57, ("The Son Who Tried to Outwit His Father"), J. H. Weeks, *Congo Life and Jungle Stories*, London, n.d. [1912?], 462. Although this story is both magical and moralizing ("a son must never think himself more powerful than his father"), there is a delightful exaggerated humor in the chain of multiple swallowings and opening ups.

FIVE IMPROBABLE TALES FROM AFRICA, p. 59, Moussa Travélé, *Proverbes et Contes Bambara*, Paris, 1923, pp. 59; 91-92; 57-58; 90-91; 101-02 (in order of presenting the stories here). Humorous dilemma stories from Mali, translated from French. LONG MEMORIES, p. 59, recalls a hoary American anecdote about English humor: An American and an Englishman were traveling together in a buggy and the American told the Englishman a joke which he finished just as they came to a bridge. A year later they were taking the same trip, and when they reached the same bridge the Englishman laughed. Are the two stories related? TWO SPEEDY PEOPLE, p. 61, had in the original a third speedy person, a woman who could cook millet in an instant rather than in the two or three hours normally required. I have also omitted a gruesome detail from the end of THE THREE GLUTTONS AND THE HUNTER, p. 65: the gluttonous hunter who licked his sword to get the taste of bean cut his tongue in two. The dilemma stories given here resemble tall tales, but most dilemma stories treat serious life situations and are told to arouse discussion and debate. They are a popular folk literature form in West Africa. For a large and fascinating collection of dilemma stories see Alta Jablow, *Yes and No, the Intimate Folklore of Africa*, Horizon Press, N.Y., 1961. "Dilemma stories," says Dr. Jablow (p. 34), "like riddles pose a problem or . . . series of problems, ranging from questions of physical or magical skills, to those of an ethical or moral nature. But knowing a riddle means knowing the answer to it. . . . The dilemma story, however, poses a problem for which there may be many answers, based on as many points of view."

THE LOUSE SKIN DRUM, p. 67, Rafael Ramirez de Arellano, *Folklore Portorriqueño,* Madrid, 1926, 52. Type 621, The Louse Skin. The story is widespread of the king or princess who fattens a louse and makes a drum or suit or dress from its skin; the princess marries the man who can guess what the object is made of. Usually, however, the riddle is solved by eavesdropping or by tricking the princess into telling the answer.

THE SHADOW, p. 69, Jon Árnason, *Icelandic Legends,* Second Series, (translated by Powell and Magnusson), London, 1884, 624. A numskull story, slightly adapted. Other, more familiar numskull stories are told in the cycle concerning the same three brothers, e.g., (1) They built a house without windows to keep the winter cold out. When summer came, they tried to carry the darkness outdoors and the sunshine indoors in their caps. (2) Coming once to a hot spring they took off their shoes and stockings and sat down round the spring to bathe their feet. But when it came time to leave they were unable to decide which feet belonged to each until a passerby to whom they called for help showed them by giving each a blow on the feet with his stick.

THE REMARKABLE OX, ROOSTER, AND DOG, p. 70, G. Taylor, "Celestial Humor, Selections from the 'Hsiao Lin Kuang' or Book of Laughter and Reminiscences," in *The China Review*, v. 14, 1885-86, pp. 87-88. A tall tale, slightly adapted. Oddly, the same story, delightfully Americanized, is reported from upstate New York in Harold W. Thompson, *Body, Boots & Britches,* J. B. Lippincott Co., 1940, 140. How did it get there? (Folktales, of course, run round the world, moving easily from one country or language to another. But they do not, ordinarily, *jump* so far.) In the New York version the "hero" boasts to a boy, "I've got an ox that can travel to Boston and back in one day. I've got some hens that can pick corn off the big beams of my barn. I've got a dog smart enough to teach school." When he sees the boy coming next day to see these wonders, he instructs his wife what to say and hides. In the Chinese version it is the wife's wit that gets her husband out of his difficulty.

THE STOLEN ROPE, p. 73, G. Taylor, *op. cit.* (under THE REMARKABLE OX, etc., above), 85. A numskull story, slightly adapted.

THE HIDDEN HOE, p. 73, a numskull tale, retold, from Herbert A. Giles, *Quips from a Chinese Jest-Book,* Shanghai, 1925, 71-72.

THE MAN IN THE MIRROR, p. 75, Edouard Chavannes, *Cinq Cents Contes et Apologues Extraits du Tripitaka Chinois,* 4 v., Paris, 1910-34, v. II, 1911, 181. A numskull story, translated from French. Folktales are widespread about numskulls seeing a mirror for the first time. In a complicated Korean story a peasant finds a mirror and amuses himself by grimacing into it. His wife wonders if he is out of his head, looks into the mirror when he is at work and decides he has taken a second wife. She shows the mirror to her wrinkled mother-in-law who, looking into it, suggests that a childless old woman has adopted him. When the father-in-law looks he says, "It's only the 'grandfather' who lives next door." Now they think, since everybody sees something different, that the mirror is dangerous and should be let alone. But the landlord's ten-year-old son comes in with a popgun, finds the mirror, scowls into it, gets angry when he sees his reflection scowl, and breaks the mirror. (André Eckhardt, *Die Ginselwurzel: Koreanische Sagen, Volkerzählungen, und Märchen,* Eisenach, 1955, 87-91.)

THE KING AND THE WRESTLER, p. 76, Subramiah Pantaluh, *Folk-Lore of the Telugus,* Madras, 1906, 7-8. A boasting trickster story from India, slightly adapted.

THE AGE OF THE ANIMALS, p. 79, Mattias Hermanns, *Himmelstier und Gletscheslöwe: Mythen, Sagen, und Fabeln aus Tibet,* Eisenach, 1955, 238-9. A story of clever boasting by animals, translated from German. Type 80A*. A different point is made in a Spanish story of this type: A bear, a wolf, and a fox found a beehive near an oak tree. The fox said, "Let the oldest have it." The wolf said, "I'm two hundred years old." The fox said, "Heavens! I was two hundred years old when this oak tree started to grow." The bear said, "I'm only eleven going on twelve, but neither one of you two had better try to eat this honey." Retold from A. M. Espinosa, *Cuentos Populares Españoles,* 3 v., Stanford University, 1923-26, v. III, 502.)

WHO AM I? p. 80, W. A. Clouston, *The Book of Noodles,* London, 1888, 7. A numskull story from a Persian jest-book, slightly adapted.

LITTLE TALL TALES, p. 82, I heard SNAKE STORY, p. 82, in Wheatland, Mo., in 1939 from an old man who used it to predict that the two parties in a lawsuit would "law and law" till they both spent everything they had. "They'll be (he said) like the two snakes that found an egg and started quarreling over it (etc.)." THE POPCORN FROST, p. 83, THE FLYING KETTLE, p. 84, SHINGLING THE FOG, p. 85, GREAT HUNTING, p. 85, BIG MOSQUITOES, p. 86, and THE PET CATFISH, p. 87, have all, in one form or another, been told, retold, reported by others, and heard by myself so often in rural America that references are unnecessary. They are among the most familiar of scores of tall tale themes. All are retold concisely without dialect.

SING SOMETHING, p. 89, N. M. Penzer, *The Ocean of Story* (C. H. Tawney's translation of Somadeva Bhatta, *Kathā Sarit Sāgara*), 10 v., London, 1924-28, v. V, 170-71. A numskull story from India, adapted. In more familiar versions of this story, a chain of men is formed to get water from a well. They fall when the topmost man spits on his hands to get a better hold on the curb.

BIG, BIG LIES! p. 90, ("Den store Løgn"), N. Levinsen, *Folkeeventyr fra Vendsyssel,* udgivet af L. Bødker, Danmarks Folkeminder, No. 68, Copenhagen, 1958, 17-21. A lying tale, translated from Danish. I have omitted some elaborate details about how Jep got the wagon tongue, doubletree and singletrees, and I have had to euphemize one aspect of the episode of landing on the fox's tail. This extraordinary story, in combining Types 1960G, The Great Tree (plants growing to heaven, etc.), and 852, The Hero Forces the Princess to Say, "That is a Lie," manages to include an astonishingly large number of both familiar and uncommon tall tale motifs and themes.

THE STORY WITHOUT AN END, p. 101, Edward Jewitt Robinson, *Tales and Poems of South India from the Tamil,* London, 1885, 381-82. An endless story, slightly adapted. A customary device for endless repetition in European and American endless tales is to have ants (or sometimes bees or locusts) carry off a huge quantity of grain, grain by grain, or to have thousands of sheep cross a stream one by one. In India the correspondingly frequent device is to have countless birds fly away, one by one, from a tree.

CARL WITHERS, noted anthropologist and folklorist, has spent over twenty-five years researching, writing, and anthologizing folklore material from all over the world, taking him to countries of Europe, South America and the Caribbean as well as much of the United States. Out of this have come many books, including favorite folklore anthologies for children: *I Saw a Rocket Walk a Mile:* Nonsense Tales, Chants and Songs from Many Lands and *A Rocket in My Pocket:* The Rhymes and Chants of Young Americans (an A.L.A. Notable Book), and two drawing folktales he adapted for the very young: *The Tale of a Black Cat* and *The Wild Ducks and the Goose. A World of Nonsense:* Strange and Humorous Tales from Many Lands is a compilation for young readers of worldwide folk nonsense stories and, like his earlier folklore anthologies, represents intensive field work and library study.

Born and raised on a Missouri farm, Mr. Withers received an A.B. degree from Harvard College and did graduate work in anthropology at Columbia University. He is well-known in this field for *Plainville, U.S.A.,* which he published under the pseudonym, James West. Now a resident of New York City, Mr. Withers is working on a number of books for readers old and young.

JOHN E. JOHNSON was raised in the heart of Pennsylvania Dutch country and graduated from the Philadelphia Museum School of Art. Now a free-lance illustrator, he lives in New York City with his wife, who is also an illustrator, and their two young children. Mr. Johnson's distinctive and captivating illustrations have animated several children's books: by Leland B. Jacobs, *Just Around the Corner* and *Is Somewhere Always Far Away;* by Carl Withers, *I Saw a Rocket Walk a Mile* and, now, *A World of Nonsense,* in which his comical drawings inventively meet the challenge of matching the absurdities of the nonsense stories.

THE BOOK is printed by offset; it has hand-lettered display type and Monophoto Bembo text type. The illustrations are pen and ink line drawings.